Acknowledgments

Thanks to the many friends and family involved.
In loving memory of John E. and Mary V. O'Donnell

Lauren Vincent-Schwinn for Book Design.
Jeff Blanchard for Editing.

With special thanks to:
Carole Monette, Anna Duart, Iris Sands, Rachel Pachter
and
Ted and Jill Rosen.

Copyright © 2000 Text, Robert J. O'Donnell
Copyright © 2005 Illustrations, Anne Rosen

Eric and Ellie Go Golfing
With Grandma and Grampy

Try to find the hidden golf ball in each illustration.

By R.J. O'Donnell

Eric and Ellie are twins, which is probably why they're alike in so many ways. One thing for sure is that they're both curious and they love to play outside. That's why they were so excited about today's date with Grampy and Grandma, who said they could all go to the course for a round of golf as soon as the weather turned nice, and today was the day, perfectly sunny in every way.

Grampy arrived to pick up the twins and they couldn't believe the way he was dressed. He was wearing a set of knickers and a little golf cap. They had never seen Grampy dressed this way before. Grampy explained to them that knickers and the golf cap were the attire often worn by golf legends and he dressed that way in memory of them.

On the way to the golf course Grampy promised to explain the game to Eric and Ellie. He also told them that he would teach them about safety on the golf course and some of the basic rules about the game and how to keep the course as beautiful as they would find it.

2

When they pulled into the parking lot, a young man immediately appeared, driving one of the really neat **golf carts**. Eric and Ellie were both very excited when they saw this. Grampy knew the young man and called him Ricky. He then told Ricky they would need 2 golf carts – one for Ellie and Grandma and one for himself and Eric. By the time Grampy got Grandma's golf clubs loaded and secured onto the back of the golf cart, Ricky had returned with another golf cart and he helped Grampy put his clubs on the back of that one.

4

Grampy and Grandma drove the carts with Eric and Ellie as passengers from the parking lot up to the cart path. Grampy explained how the gas pedal and the brake worked, and showed Eric the switch that worked forward and reverse.

6

After parking the carts in the proper area, they all went into the Clubhouse.

Everyone seemed to know Grampy and Grandma and they were very happy to meet Eric and Ellie. They told them that they were glad they were there and hoped that they enjoyed their round of golf. Grampy went into the **pro shop** *(a small store with golf clothes and golf equipment).* Grampy let the pro know that he was there and confirmed his **tee-time,** *(the term used for what time players start a round of golf at the first tee).*

Grandma bought Ellie a visor and Eric a ball cap, and soon it was time to go see the **starter.**

The **starter,** who Grampy said Eric and Ellie could call Mr. Wagner, showed them where the first **tee box** was and said they were "Next up!" after the four golfers who were on the tee. Grampy and Grandma then took some golf balls out of their golf bags and made marks on them with a magic marker so that they would know whose ball was whose. Grampy put three black dots on his, and Grandma put two red dots on hers. Grampy said, "This way, our balls will not get confused with someone else's whose might land near ours on the course." Grampy also handed Grandma a whole bunch of **golf tees** and a little **repair tool** that he said was used to fix ball marks on the putting greens, that he would show Eric and Ellie how to use very soon.

10

Grampy took the **score card** that Mr. Wagner had given him and showed Eric and Ellie how it listed the holes on the golf course. Grampy went on to explain that if you hit the ball and it went right in the hole, that was called a **Hole in One**.

He then explained, that **par** meant the number of shots it was supposed to take to get the ball in the hole. Some holes are designed to be par threes, some are par fours, and some are par fives.

He further explained that every shot is called a **stroke,** and if you get the ball in the hole in two strokes under par, it's known as an **Eagle**. If you get the ball in the hole in one stroke under par, it is a **Birdie**. If it takes one more stroke than it should to get the ball in the hole, it is a **Bogie**, two more strokes is a "**Double Bogie**," and three strokes a **Triple Bogie**.

Ellie asked, "What do you call it if it took four extra strokes to get the ball in the hole?" Grandma smiled and said "If there are people behind you and you've hit the ball that many times, it's probably best to just pick it up, put it in your pocket and move on to the next hole."

Eric and Grampy laughed when Grandma said that about picking up the ball. Grandma explained that it is always important to pay attention to the pace at which you are playing the game so that you are not holding up the people behind you. She said, "This is one of the rules of courtesy on the golf course that you'll learn today." They were now ready to start and Grampy and Grandma advanced the carts up to the first tee box, the area on each hole where you make your first shot.

The tee box on the first hole had three sets of **markers: red, white**, and **blue**. The red markers were closest to the putting green that we were aiming for, with the white ones in the middle and the blue ones the furthest back.

Grandma told Eric and Ellie, "Generally, women hit from the red tees, and men use the other two sets of tees, depending on their skill level." She went on to explain that this red, white and blue system is also used with what they call **"fairway markings."** She said, "Some courses may be different, but on this course, we have markers in the middle of the fairway that we'll point out to you as we go along." She said the red ones meant 100 yards from the middle of the putting green, the white ones meant 150 yards from the middle of the putting green, and the blue ones meant 200 yards from the middle of the putting green.

Eric and Ellie were starting to think there was an awful lot to learn about this game and they wondered how they would remember everything.

Grampy stepped up onto the tee and told Eric and Ellie that they should stand beside the tee and be very quiet. Grampy told us that when people are teeing off, everyone is very quiet and careful to give the golfer plenty of room to take practice swings so that no one would get hurt with a club. **"Safety is always important on the golf course!!!"**

The first hole was a 340-yard par 4 for Grampy and a 300-yard par 4 for Grandma. That meant that the red tee markers were 40 yards closer to the hole than the white ones that Grampy was going to hit from. Both Grandma and Grampy decided to use the biggest clubs in their bags, which they called their **drivers**.

After taking a couple of practice swings, Grampy teed up his ball at the white markers and hit it straight down the middle, almost 200 yards! Then Grandma walked up to the red tees and hit her ball right down the middle and it landed close to Grampy's ball. Grandma would get to shoot next because she was farther away from the hole than he was, and the person furthest from the hole usually goes next.

Grandma's golf ball was just a few yards in front of the white fairway marker. Grandma explained to us that this meant she was probably about 140 to 145 yards from the flag on the putting green. The **flagstick**, which some people call the **pin**, is in the **hole** or **cup**. Grandma took the number four **iron** out of her bag and said, "If I can hit this the way I'm supposed to, I should be able to get the ball on the putting green." She was right! She swung nice and easy, hit the ball high and very straight, and it landed right on the green. Grampy said, "Great shot Grandma! I hope I can do as well."

For his second shot, Grampy used his seven **iron.** He hit his ball higher in the air than Grandma did but it went right and landed in a **bunker**, which looked like a big sand-box. He didn't seem too happy about that. Grampy's ball was further away from the hole than Grandma's, which was on the green, so Grampy had to shoot next.

He took his **sand wedge** out of his bag and stepped gingerly down into the sand. He was very careful not to **ground** his club.

He explained that was something you're not allowed to do before you hit the ball. He swung very hard and the ball came right up and out and sailed over the pin, but when it hit the green, it stopped short, about ten feet past the hole.

Then Grampy picked up a rake that was lying beside the sand, and smoothed over where he had swung his club and where he had left footprints. He then let Eric finish.

18

The putting green, also called the **green** for short, was *very* beautiful. The grass was short and a different color than normal grass. They keep the grass like this so that the ball rolls smoothly and easily. The first thing Grampy did was take out his **repair tool,** which was shaped like a horseshoe, and fix the marks that were made by his, and Grandma's golf balls, when they hit the green.

Grandma's golf ball was about twelve feet from the hole, so it was her turn to hit. Grampy asked "Do you want me to tend the **flagstick**?" *(he would hold the pin so she could see where the hole was and then pull it out after she hit her ball).* "Why not let Ellie do it?" Grandma said." Then she hit her ball straight at the cup, but not hard enough to go in.

"Nicely done Grandma", Grampy said, "would you like to finish putting?" "Yes," she answered *(that's another kind of golf courtesy, where the player gets to finish putting even though they're not closer to the hole).* Her fourth stroke put the ball right in the cup, so Grandma made a par, and they all clapped.

Next, Grampy tried to get his fourth stroke in the cup but he hit the ball too hard and it went three feet past. He was able to get it in on his fifth shot and said, "I'll take the bogie."

They proceeded to the next **tee-box**. Grandma brought to our attention the board beside the tee that was a diagram of the second hole. She explained that this hole was a "par five," **dog leg** right. *(That meant that **par** equaled five strokes on this hole.)* She showed us on the diagram what a **dog leg** right meant. The hole itself was around the corner from the tee-box on the right hand side. The picture on the board really did look like the leg of a dog! Grandma said, "This is a good hole for the players that **slice** the ball off the tee."

Eric asked Grandma what she meant by **slicing the ball,** and she explained, that it's the term one uses when the ball goes to the right, for a right handed golfer, and if a left-handed golfer slices the ball, it would go to the left.

Ellie asked Grandma if there was a name for when the ball goes in the opposite direction. Grandma said, "That's a very good question Ellie! Yes there is. If a right handed golfer hits the ball to the left, it's called **hooking the ball.**"

Grampy said, "O.K., the people in front of us are far enough away for me to play now."
He explained, that you always have to be very careful to make sure that if there are people
playing in front of you, they're far enough ahead of you, that you don't hit them with your
ball, or even distract them while they are playing.

Grampa also said, that if you do hit your ball close to other golfers it is very important to
yell "fore!" to warn them that you are there. But if you do hit into a group by accident, it
is very important say "sorry" afterward.

Grandma, having won the first hole with a par, had the right to tee-off first. She said, "It's
my honors, but why don't you go ahead and hit first Grampy, and then we can all drive
down to the ladies' tee."

Grampy hit straight down the middle, and exclaimed, "That felt good! I'll bet'cha that's out
there two hundred yards!". He still had a long way to go because this hole was 530 yards
long from the white tees.

Eric and Ellie really loved riding in the golf carts. Grandma went ahead, and hit her ball well this time, in the fairway to the left of Grampy's ball, and nearly as far. She was going to take the next stroke.

As Eric and Ellie rode in the carts up to the balls, they could now see around the corner, and noticed the green was still a long way away, and up on a hill. In order to get to the green, Grandma and Grampy were going to have to hit over a large body of water.

Eric and Ellie could see ducks swimming in the water and hoped that nobody would hit them with their balls. "If you do hit a golf ball into the water," Grampy explained, "you have to drop a new ball on the grass close to where it went in, and you have to add one stroke to your score." *(He called this a **penalty stroke**)*. He explained, that there are many ways to end up getting penalty strokes during the course of playing the game, and he would try to explain them as we went along.

Both Grandma and Grampy hit clubs that looked very much like the **drivers** they used on the tee, but were **fairway woods.** Grandma said that her "3 wood" was built to give the ball more loft *(or height),* when she hit it. It was easier to hit off the grass than her driver would be, without the benefit of a tee which is only used on the **tee box**. Grandma and Grampy were both very lucky as they both were able to hit their balls over the water, *(and the ducks, too).*

28

After they drove around the pond, it took Grampy and Grandma each two strokes to get their balls onto the green. Grampy tried to hit his five iron really hard, but he hit a little bit behind the golf ball, made a big **divot,** and the ball didn't go very far. Grampy said, "My goodness! My divot went almost as far as my ball!"

He picked up the divot and placed it back where it was, and then pressed it down with his foot. He told Eric and Ellie, "It's very important to always replace your divots and repair any damage that you make to the grass from either your practice swings or your actual shots." Grampy again repaired the marks that the balls had made on the green.

It took Grandma three shots to get her ball into the cup, and it only took Grampy one stroke. It was a very long putt that he made. He was very excited and said that he didn't often get a par on that hole.

Grandma, who took seven shots to get the ball into the cup, had a **"double bogie"** and she said to Ellie and Eric "That's how I score on this hole almost every time I play it."

32

Eric and Ellie were having a great time because they were seeing all kinds of different birds, squirrels, ducks, and even a whole flock of geese. They realized, having never been on a golf course before, how much fun it was to see all the different animals darting out of the trees and the woods. Grampy told them, on some golf courses in New England, there are foxes, and on some golf courses in the Southeastern United States there are alligators and crocodiles.

Ellie didn't think it would be much fun to run into alligators and crocodiles when trying to play golf, and Grandma agreed.

The next hole that they played was hole No. 3, and it reminded Eric and Ellie of the hole they had just played, No. 2, except that it bent around the corner to the left and it was a par 4.

They ran into Jim and Artie, who they knew because their older sister, Morgan, went to high school with them. The boys were surprised to see them out on the golf course and explained that they were there **caddying** for their dads, who were playing a match. *(Caddying means carrying the players clubs and keeping an eye on the player's golf ball).* Artie told Eric that he should consider going to caddy camp, and caddying in the summer to make extra money. He said, "The next time I come over to your house to see Morgan, I'll tell you all about it. But right now, I have to pay attention to my dad's tee-shot."

36

The fourth hole was almost like the first hole in that it was long, straight, and a par four. However, nobody would ever believe what happened on this hole. After Grampy and Grandma hit their drives, which landed in the fairway, they started driving down the **cart path**. All of a sudden, out of nowhere, a seagull swept down onto the fairway, picked up Grandma's ball, and flew away with it, toward the coast. They all started laughing and Grandma said, "I've never seen anything like that in my life!" But Grampy told the children he had actually seen it happen once on television, during one of the big **PGA** *(Professional Golf Association)* tournaments. He told Grandma that she could drop a ball where her ball was, and not be penalized. *(The seagull must have thought that Grandma's ball looked like a clam, but dropped it into the tall grass near the water.)* Grandma reached into her pocket and pulled out another ball. "We'll have a good story for the Clubhouse later!" she said.

38

On the fifth hole, Eric and Ellie got to use the golf ball washer. Grampy said, "Its important you keep your ball clean, because it not only helps you find it, but a clean ball is a happy ball." And they all laughed after that.

The tee box was up the hill and the kids could see the green way off in the distance. This hole was also a par four and Grampy said, "It looks longer than it really is, because we are up so high." Eric and Ellie smiled and laughed with each other because the golf cart path almost looked like a roller coaster ride, bending and turning around the hill and between the trees all the way to the bottom.

40

Eric and Ellie noticed a black and white lighthouse that looked very familiar. Then they realized that this was the same lighthouse that they had toured the summer before with their parents. They remembered how much they had enjoyed that adventure because they had never been in a lighthouse, and this one actually works 24 hours a day, sending bright beams of light across the horizon for all the boaters to see.

When they got to the sixth hole, they were looking up a hill at the green. They thought it was funny that Grampy and Grandma just hit their balls down a hill only now to be hitting them up a different hill. Grandma told Ellie and Eric that most courses have eighteen holes. The holes are usually divided in half. They are called the **front nine** and the **back nine.** Grandma said they usually walk when they only play nine holes. Ellie was surprised that Grandma liked walking up and down all those hills and Grandma explained that it was a good way for her and Grampy to get exercise. Eric said to Ellie, "I'm sure glad to ride in the golf carts instead of walking!"

The seventh hole was another straight away par four. What made this one hard, was a big stream that runs right across the fairway and half-way between the tee-box and the green. This meant it was very easy to roll the ball into the stream, unless you could hit the ball far enough to go over it. What Ellie liked about the hole was the pretty wooden bridges on each side of the fairway that cross the stream. On Grandma's second stroke, she hit her ball into the water, next to the bridge. Ellie stood on the bridge and watched as Eric took off his sneakers and socks and waded into the water to retrieve Grandma's ball. Eric was very excited because he actually found four other balls while he was in the stream.

Grampy laughed and said, "You could have used this!" and he showed us a neat thing that he called a **"ball retriever."** It was a telescopic pole with a cup on the end to pick up balls.

Grampy won this hole with a par and Grandma got a double bogie. Grampy was delighted and said to the twins, "It's a good thing I won that hole because Grandma and I are all tied up now."

44

On the eighth hole, Grampy teed his ball up and tried to hit it so hard that it went very deep into the woods on the right hand side. "Boy, oh boy, did I ever slice that one!" he exclaimed. "I couldn't find that ball in a million years, let alone the five minutes that I am allowed to look for it." So he hit another one that he called a **provisional,** and explained to them, "that where the ball fell on the fairway he now had a **lie** three". He had hit the ball once that went into the woods and now he had to take a penalty stroke for losing it, as well as loose the distance, he had originally hit from. He had to hit a new ball from the tee-box so that was really his third shot. He said, "Oh boy, your Grandma's probably going to win this hole," and she did, by scoring a five that was a bogie. Grampy ended up with an eight. He said, "After hitting the ball poorly twice, and then three putting, I'll take a **snowman.**"

The children didn't know what he meant until Grandma pointed out that the eight on the score card looks like a snowman. So now, Grandma was one hole up, with one hole to go. She told us that the way they played was by who won the most holes. The professionals play by counting the number of strokes, so she was excited because she couldn't lose. Grampy reminded her that the next hole was a par three, that he always did well on, and planned on tying up the match.

46

The ninth hole itself was very beautiful. It was one hundred yards for Grandma from the ladies' tee and one hundred sixty yards for Grampy from the white tees. The good golfers who would normally play from the blue tees, would have to hit the ball two hundred and five yards to reach the green. The green had water half way around the left-hand side with a waterfall in the back, and bunkers all the way around the right hand side and one right in front. Grampy explained to us that they call this the **signature hole.** He said "Some courses designate the prettiest hole on the golf course as their signature hole." He went on to point out that the dining room, which was upstairs from the pro shop, overlooked the green. People in the dining room were able to see the golfers hitting their balls off the tee, and then finishing up the hole, putting. "This is one hole," he said, "where you don't want to go into the bunkers or into the water on the left because everyone is watching you." Grandma said, "That always makes me nervous." "You'd be a lot more nervous if you were hitting from the men's tees", Grampy said. They all laughed.

48

Grampy chose his four iron which he said was his one hundred sixty-yard club. The lower the number on the iron, the farther the ball goes, because of the angle on the club. In his golf bag, he had irons numbered three through nine and two **"wedges."** He uses the wedges to get out of thick grass on short shots and to get out of bunkers. He said, "I hope I don't have to use anything but my putter after my tee shot", and he didn't. He hit the ball, straight and only about four feet from the cup. Grandma used her eight iron and put her ball right on the green as well. Grandma and Grampy each congratulated each other on two excellent golf shots. When they got up to the green some of the people who were standing around told Grandma and Grampy how nice their shots were.

Grampy put his **ball marker,** which looked like a big thumb tack, right behind his ball, then picked the ball up. Now, the ball was not in Grandma's way and would not distract her.

50

Grandma had very long putt that almost went in the hole, but rolled about a foot past. She approached the ball while the people standing around the green clapped for her. She tapped it in for her par and then bowed to the onlookers as if she had just won a big match, which it was, for us... no matter who won.

Grampy replaced his ball in front of his marker and said, "Now the pressure is really on me, I need to sink this putt for a birdie just to tie Grandma." Ellie said to Grandma, "We bet all the people watching Grampy putt will make him nervous", to which Grandma replied "He's usually pretty good under pressure." Sure enough Grampy slowly pulled back his putter and followed through nice and easy, and they all watched the ball roll right into the middle of the cup and drop. Grampy was very excited and exclaimed, "YES! BIRDIE!". He went and gave Grandma a hug and said, "Nice round."

Eric and Ellie enjoyed the morning so much on the golf course that they asked Grampy if they could continue to play the "back nine." "Believe me," Grampy said "we'd love to, but it will have to be another time, we have to get you home now. We'll come back again soon."

Grampy and Grandma signed their score card and brought it into the pro shop, where they turned it in. While they were in the pro shop, Grampy bought each Eric and Ellie a **"USGA Rules of Golf"** handbook to keep as a souvenir.

On the way to the parking lot, Grampy showed us the green where people practice their putting and the **driving range** where people can practice hitting all their clubs. Grandma said, "If you children are interested in learning how to play golf, I'll talk to your parents and if it's all right with them, I'll arrange for you to take a lesson. There are a lot of golf scholarships available for boys and girls."

Eric and Ellie seemed very excited at this prospect and hoped that their next adventure would be learning how to play golf themselves.

WATCH FOR THE NEXT ADVENTURE OF ERIC AND ELLIE WHEN THEY MEET THEIR GOLF INSTRUCTOR AND LEARN THE FUNDAMENTALS OF THE GAME.

Things we've learned

I. **Glossary of Terms**

II. **Courtesy Issues**

III. **Golf Course Repair Issues**

IV. **Distance Markers**

V. **Equipment & Tools**

VI. **Penalties**

 PROUDLY MADE IN THE USA Printed in the USA by TanaSeybert New York